Underwater Chase

Tony Bradman • Jon Stuart

Contents

OXFORD
UNIVERSITY PRESS

Macro Marvel
(billionaire inventor)

Welcome to Micro World!

Macro Marvel invented Micro World – a micro-sized theme park where you have to shrink to get in.

A computer called **CODE** controls Micro World and all the robots inside – MITEs and BITEs.

A MITE

A BITE

Disaster strikes!

CODE goes wrong on opening day.
CODE wants to shrink the world.

Macro Marvel is trapped inside the park ...

Enter Team X!

Four micro agents – *Max, Cat, Ant* and *Tiger* – are sent to rescue Macro Marvel and defeat CODE.

Mini Marvel joins Team X.

Mini Marvel
(Macro's daughter)

In the last book ...

- Max and Ant dived underwater to find the CODE key.

- The Octo-BITE trapped Ant with its tentacle. Max rescued him.

- Max and Ant hid from the BITE in a sunken ship.

**CODE key
(5 collected)**

You are in the Shark Dive zone.

3

Before you read

Sound checker
Say the sounds.

ir   ew

ou

Sound spotter
Blend the sounds.

y	ou

ch	ew	s

h	ur	t

s	qu	ir	t	s

Tricky words
people
work

Into the zone
Who do you think will look
for Max and Ant?

4

The Octo-BITE

"We need to look for Max and Ant," said Cat. "I hope they aren't hurt." "Let's find out about the new BITE first," said Mini.

Octo-BITE

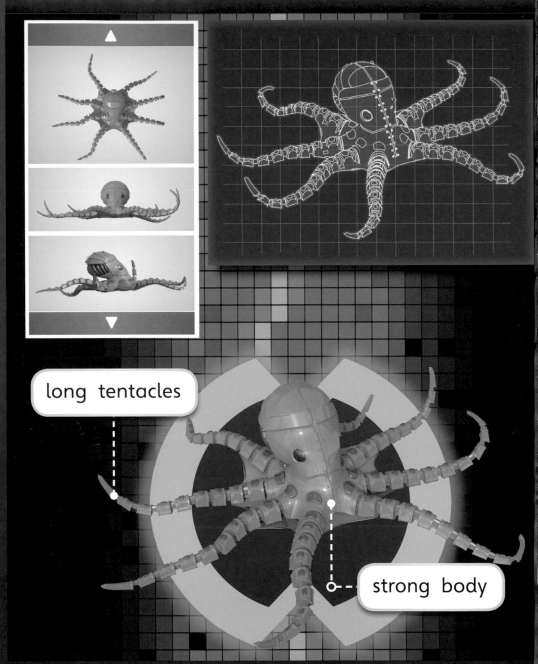

long tentacles

strong body

Attack!

Speed | Strength | Combat | Fright

It chews crabs, fish ... and people!

poison ink

squirts ink

It can grab people.

Stop the BITE!

CODE key

The CODE key is screwed onto the BITE's head.
You need to turn it a few times to get it off.

"Right," said Cat. "It's time to get to work. I may need to rescue Max and Ant."

"I will dive with you, too," said Tiger.

Now you have read ...
The Octo-BITE

Take a closer look
What features does this page have?
Find the heading, picture and labels.
Explain what they are for.

Thinking time
At the beginning of the story, Mini said,
"Let's find out about the new BITE first."
Why do you think she said that? Was it
a good idea?

> How can I find Max and Ant?

11

Before you read

Sound checker
Say the sounds.

ir   ew

ou

Sound spotter
Blend the sounds.

f	ew

c	l	ue

wh	ir	l	ed

g	r	ou	p

Tricky word
water

Into the zone

Where were Max and
Ant hiding?

12

Trapped!

Max and Ant had shrunk and were hiding from the BITE in the ship. "Do you think the BITE is still out there?" said Max.

"I haven't got a clue," said Ant.

Whoosh! The BITE's tentacle burst through the porthole.

It whirled around in the water. The BITE was looking for Max and Ant.

The BITE was squirting ink.

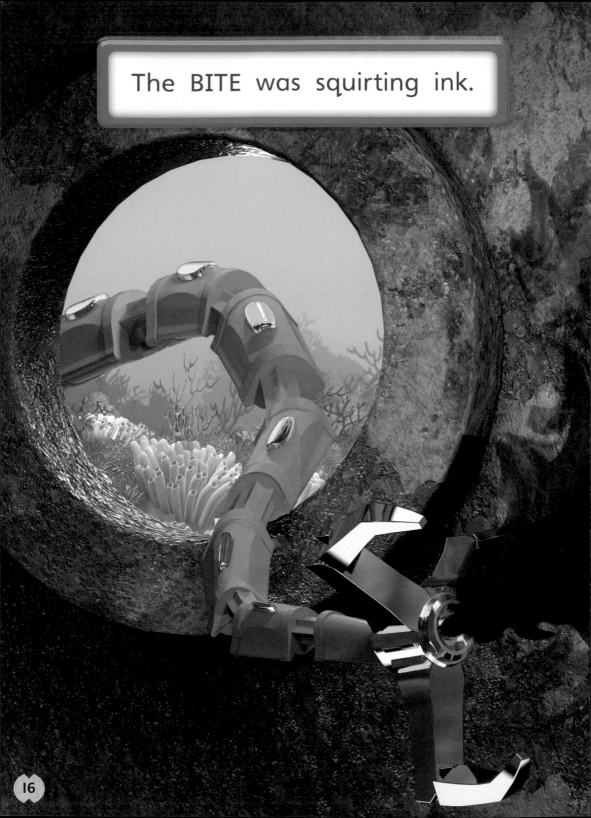

Max and Ant darted out of the way.

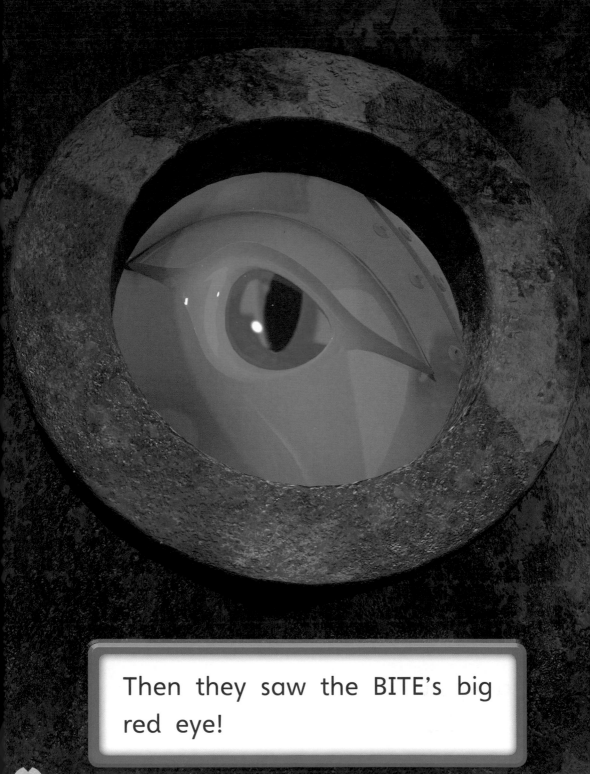

Then they saw the BITE's big red eye!

Max and Ant had to find a new hiding place. They went deeper into the ship.

They found a few boxes in the crew's cabin. One was full of jewels!

They swam into the box. The lid snapped shut. They were trapped. "We're doomed!" cried Ant.

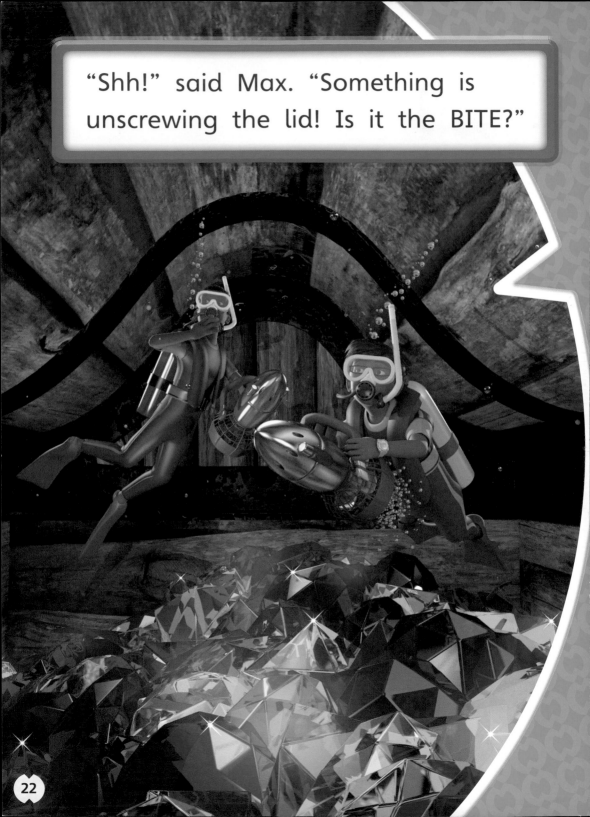

"Shh!" said Max. "Something is unscrewing the lid! Is it the BITE?"

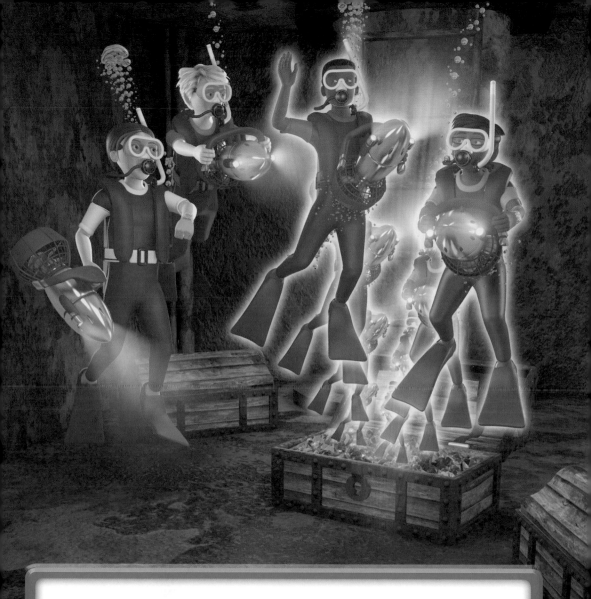

"Phew! It's you two," said Ant. Cat had tracked them on her watch. "Girl to the rescue!" she said. "I'm glad our group is safe!"

Now you have read ...
Trapped!

Whoosh!

Text checker
What is happening in this picture?
Look back at the story to find
more words that describe
sounds or movements.

Thinking time
How do you think Max and
Ant felt when Cat opened the
lid of the box?

How did I find
Max and Ant?